National Curriculum
Key Stage 2 Age 10–11

Practice Papers

Key Stage 2
National Tests

SCIENCE

How the Key Stage 2 National Tests will affect your child

- All pupils in Year 6 (age 10–11) will take National Tests in English, Mathematics and Science. These important tests are held in May each year and are designed to be an objective assessment of the work your child will have done during Key Stage 2 of the National Curriculum.

- Pupils will also have their school work assessed by their teachers. These teacher assessments will be set alongside your child's results in the National Tests to give a clear picture of his/her overall achievement.

- In July, the results of your child's tests together with the teacher assessments will be reported to you.

- Results from these tests will be used in the compilation of school 'league tables'.

- It is not the purpose of the tests to aid secondary schools in deciding which children to give places to, but the results may be used to help place your child in the appropriate teaching group.

How this book will help your child

- This book offers plenty of practice in the type of question your child will face in the Key Stage 2 National Test for Science.

- An explanation of the core curriculum topics shows you what your child needs to know.

- The answers and a mark scheme have been provided to allow you to check how your child has done.

- The 'Note to parent' boxes in the Answers section give you advice on how to improve your child's answers and avoid common mistakes.

- A unique Marking grid allows you to record your child's results and estimate the level of the National Curriculum at which your child is working.

The test questions, answers and 'Notes to parent' contained in this publication are based upon the official test materials provided to schools, but do not reproduce those tests exactly. The official tests are supported by administrative and other guidance for teachers to use in setting the tests, marking them and interpreting their results. The results your child achieves in taking the tests in this book may not be the same as he/she achieves in the official tests.

Every effort has been made to trace copyright holders and to obtain their permission for the use of copyright material. The authors and publishers will gladly receive any information enabling them to rectify any error or omission in subsequent editions.

First published 1995
Revised 1995, 1997 (twice), 1998, 1999, 2001, 2002, 2003
Reprinted 1996, 1998

Text: © Bob McDuell and Graham Booth 1999, 2002
Design and illustrations: © Letts Educational Limited 2001, 2002

Series editor: Bob McDuell

British Library Cataloguing in Publication Data
A CIP record for this book is available from the British Library

ISBN 1 84315 061 1

Cover design by 2idesign, Cambridge
Cover logo by Starfish Design for Print, London
Project management and typesetting by Hardlines Ltd, Charlbury, Oxford

Printed in Italy

Letts Educational Ltd
The Chiswick Centre
414 Chiswick High Road
London
W4 5TF
Telephone: 020 8996 3333
Fax: 020 8742 8390
email: mail@lettsed.co.uk
website: www.letts-education.com

Letts Educational Limited is a member of Granada Learning Limited, part of Granada plc.

Contents

What you need to know about the National Tests

What is the purpose of National Tests?

The tests, taken by pupils in Year 6, have several functions:

- they provide the government with a snapshot picture of attainment throughout the country, enabling it to make judgements about whether standards are improving nationally;
- they give information to OFSTED about schools' achievements, so that they can judge which schools are improving and which are deemed to be failing their pupils;
- they give you information about your child's progress compared to national standards.

How do the tests work?

In May of Year 6, your child will take tests on the core subjects of English, Mathematics and Science. In Science there are two tests. Your child will have 45 minutes to complete each test. The tests are not marked in school by a teacher, but posted off to an external marker, who is often a teacher in another school or a retired teacher. External markers have been trained in marking the tests so that all pupils' test papers throughout the country are marked to the same standard.

Once the tests have been marked, the mark is translated into a 'level'. The level that each mark corresponds to is decided according to results gained in pre-tests and the tests themselves. It varies slightly from year to year. The test papers, marks and levels are returned to your child's school in July, then the levels are reported to you and to the secondary school that your child will attend.

What do the tests assess?

The tests are designed to assess your child's knowledge, skills and understanding in the context of the programme of study set out in the National Curriculum. This can be found on the National Curriculum website, www.nc.uk.net. The programme of study is divided into four sections, called Attainment Targets:

- Sc1 – Scientific enquiry – ideas and evidence in science and investigative skills.
- Sc2 – Life processes and living things – animals and plants and their environments.
- Sc3 – Materials and their properties – grouping and changing materials and separating mixtures.
- Sc4 – Physical processes – forces, electricity, light and sound.

Questions in the tests cover all four Attainment Targets, but the questions about scientific enquiry (Sc1) are usually set within the context of one of the other Attainment Targets.

What are the levels and what do they mean?

There is a set of benchmark standards that measure a pupil's progress through the first three Key Stages of the National Curriculum. Attainment is measured in steps called 'levels', from 1 to 7. The National Curriculum document sets out the knowledge, skills and understanding that pupils should demonstrate at each level. The government target is for pupils to achieve level 2 at the end of Key Stage 1, level 4 at the end of Key Stage 2 and level 5 or 6 at the end of Key Stage 3. The chart below shows these government targets.

At the end of Key Stage 2, pupils take the tests targeted at levels 3 to 5. Pupils achieving very high marks within level 5 are assessed as Gifted and Talented children.

How does this book help my child?

This book gives your child practice in answering the type of question that he/she will face in the actual tests. By practising questions in this way, your child will feel under less pressure and be more relaxed. Being relaxed helps pupils to perform at their best in tests, so we have targeted the questions at levels 3–5, allowing your child to become familiar with most of the types of question that are asked in the tests.

The tests in this book are longer than the SAT tests to give your child the widest range of possible questions.

How your child should progress

Preparing and practising for the Science Test

The questions in this book test the same things as the actual test papers:

- knowledge
- understanding
- handling information
- interpreting information and data
- solving problems
- using experiments to test ideas.

What are the key features of this book?

This book contains all you need to prepare your child for the tests:

- National Curriculum requirements – key information for each of the Attainment Targets Sc1, Sc2, Sc3 and Sc4.
- Questions – two practice test papers targeted at Levels 3–5.
- Answers – showing the responses that will gain credit in the tests and how the marks are allocated.
- 'Note to parent' boxes – advice as to how you can improve your child's performance.
- Level charts – what the marks mean in terms of National Curriculum levels.

How should I use this book?

Well in advance of the tests, suggest to your child that some practice might be a good idea. Make sure that he/she is in comfortable surroundings and has all the necessary equipment (pen, pencil, rubber and ruler). Spend some time making sure that your child understands the instructions for completing the test, and then leave your child alone for the specified time (75 minutes) to complete Test A. During this time, be available to help read any difficult words or interpret instructions, but do not look over your child's shoulder as this may prevent him/her from concentrating fully.

After your child has completed the test, work through the paper along with the answers and advice at the back of the book. Record your child's marks in the top half of the boxes in the margin. Work out the total marks gained for each question, write them in the grid on page 79 and add them up to arrive at the total mark for the paper. You can then use the charts on page 78 to determine the level of your child's performance on this test.

Before your child attempts Test B, it is a good idea to highlight or make a note of areas where your child did not do well, so that he/she can revise these. Avoid extensive criticism, as this will allow your child to appreciate any suggestions as to how he/she may improve. You could encourage your child to write brief revision notes as a memory aid.

A few weeks later, allow your child to take Test B using a similar procedure as with Test A. The marks and level that your child achieves this time will inform you as to his/her progress and identify any remaining areas of weakness. Use simple models and diagrams to explain ideas that your child does not understand and then encourage your child to write down his/her own explanations.

Questions marked with a diamond (◆) are testing aspects of Sc1.

What does the level mean?

The tests in this book give a guide as to the level that your child is likely to achieve in the actual tests. We hope that, through practice, these tests will give your child the confidence to achieve his/her best. By working through the answers with your child, you should be able to improve his/her achievement.

How do I help my child prepare to take the actual tests?

A few days before the test:

- work through the questions in Tests A and B again, making sure that your child understands the correct answers to each question;

- check that your child knows which test papers he/she will be taking and when these are to be sat;

- double check that your child has the necessary equipment, including a spare pen and pencil.

Finally, avoid putting your child under pressure and reassure him/her about any worries that he/she may have.

National Curriculum requirements

The next few pages give you information about the knowledge required at each level for the Attainment Targets, plus some practice questions to help you focus.

Sc1 Scientific enquiry: Requirements at each level

Level 1 Describe simple features of objects, living things and events. Communicate these descriptions orally and by drawings.

Level 2 Respond to suggestions about how questions can be answered by referring to books and collecting data. Compare the features of different objects and living things. Make a comparison between the outcome of an event and what was expected to happen.

Level 3 Suggest how questions can be answered. Make simple observations and measurements and record these. Recognise and explain simple patterns in observations and measurements and explain the importance of fair testing.

Level 4 Decide on the best approach to answer a question. Plan and carry out a fair test after predicting the outcome, using secondary sources of information where appropriate. Use simple graphs and charts to present results and show patterns. Explain their results and suggest how the procedure could be improved.

LIFE PROCESSES AND LIVING THINGS (Sc2)

Life processes that are common to plants and animals include:
- **growth** – young plants and animals need to grow to become adult;
- **nutrition** – food is needed for energy and growth;
- **reproduction** – new plants and animals are needed to replace those that die.

Teeth are important in the digestive process. Humans have three types of teeth:
- **incisors** – the sharp teeth at the front of the mouth that cut food;
- **molars** – the teeth at the back of the mouth that grind the food into small pieces;
- **canines** – used for ripping and tearing meat.

Digested food and oxygen circulate around the body in **blood**, which is pumped through the body and the lungs by the **heart**. The rate at which the heart beats is measured by the pulse rate; this increases when more glucose and oxygen is needed due to exercise and slows down when the body is resting.

Animals such as humans can move around because they have:
- a **skeleton** – the bones that support and protect the body;
- **muscles** – their action makes bones move when we walk and lift things.

All new life starts with **fertilisation**. A new human grows as an **embryo** before being **born**. It passes through the stages of **childhood**, **adolescence** and **adulthood** when it is able to reproduce.

A plant begins to grow when the seed **germinates**; after growth it develops sex organs in the flower. Transfer of **pollen** from the male organ to the female organ may result in fertilisation of an **egg** in the **ovary**. The fertilised eggs then develop into seeds.

Important parts of a plant include:
- the **leaves** – this is where energy from sunlight is used to make food;
- the **roots** – these anchor the plant and take in water and nutrients from the soil.

The plants and animals that live in a **habitat** depend on each other for food. This can be shown by a **food chain** that shows which animals eat plants and which eat other animals. Almost all food chains start with a green plant, because plants make their own food.

Micro-organisms also exist in a habitat. They are essential for **decomposing** dead material and returning the nutrients to the ground. Some of these micro-organisms are harmful to humans and other animals as they cause disease.

Sc2 Life processes and living things: Requirements at each level

Level 1 Name the parts of the human body and of a plant. Identify common animals such as fly, goldfish or robin.

Level 2 Describe the conditions needed for plants and animals to survive. Group plants and animals using simple features. Know that different plants and animals live in different habitats.

Level 3 Describe differences between living and non-living things. Explain how changes in living things might occur and recognise how an animal is adapted to its environment.

Level 4 Identify the major organs and organ systems of the human body and of a plant. Use keys to identify and group living things. Use a food chain to describe a feeding relationship.

Level 5 Describe the functions of the organs of the human body and of a plant. Compare the life cycles of an animal and of a plant. Explain why different organisms are found in different habitats and why living things need to be classified.

Quick questions

1 Making new living things is called ....

2 The teeth at the front of the mouth are the ....

3 The heart pumps ....through the body.

4 Humans can stand upright because they have a ....

5 Which part of a plant keeps it fixed in the ground?

....

6 Which part of a plant transports water from the root to the leaf?

....

7 What do all food chains start with?

....

8 Which body organ filters the blood?

....

9 The two **most** important substances that the blood carries around the body are?

.... and ....

10 In which part of a plant is food made?

....

MATERIALS AND THEIR PROPERTIES (Sc3)

Materials have different properties.
These properties include:

- **hardness** – how firm the material is;
- **strength** – how big a force the material can withstand;
- **flexibility** – whether a material bends easily;
- **magnetism** – whether it is attracted to a magnet.

Materials are chosen for a particular use because of their suitable properties. For example, copper is used for electric wiring because it is flexible and conducts electricity well. It is also easily drawn into a wire.

The clothes that we wear in winter keep us warm because they are good thermal **insulators**.

All substances can exist in three states, depending upon the conditions:

- **solids** have a fixed shape and volume;
- **liquids** also have a fixed volume and take up the shape of the bottom of the container;
- **gases** fill the whole container and take up its shape and volume.

Liquids, powders and some gases can be poured.

The diagram shows the names given to changes in state.

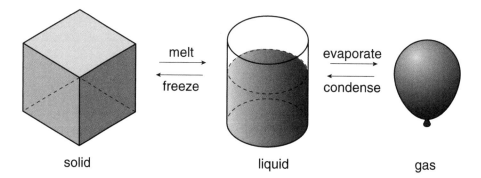

| solid | liquid | gas |

These changes can all be undone – they are **reversible**. Dissolving salt in water is another reversible change – the salt can be recovered by evaporating the water. **Non-reversible** changes are used to make new materials. When bread dough is heated in the oven the dough hardens and turns into bread. This change cannot be reversed. Changes involving **burning** cannot be reversed.

Mixtures of materials can be separated in different ways:

- **sieving** can separate solids of different size particles;
- **dissolving** can separate solids where one (such as salt) dissolves and the other (such as sand) does not;
- **filtering** can separate a liquid from a solid that does not dissolve.

Quick questions

In each of the following lists, one material is the odd one out. Which is the odd one out in each list and what property makes it odd?

1 copper   gold   iron   wood ....

2 cooking oil   ice   petrol   water ....

3 granite   marble   steel   wood ....

4 instant coffee   salt   sand   sugar ....

5 candle wax   petrol   water   wood ....

Choose words from this list to describe the changes below:

burn   condense   dissolve   evaporate   freeze   melt

6 Ice becomes water. ....

7 Steam becomes water. ....

8 Oil catches fire. ....

9 Solid candle wax becomes liquid. ....

10 Which of the changes 6–9 are reversible and which are non-reversible?

....

A **circuit** is a complete conducting path from the positive to the negative side of a battery or power supply. A **switch** turns things off by breaking the circuit.

The brightness of a bulb in a circuit depends on the **current**:
- adding more batteries or increasing the voltage makes the bulb brighter;
- adding more bulbs in series makes them dimmer.

These are common **symbols** used in circuit diagrams:

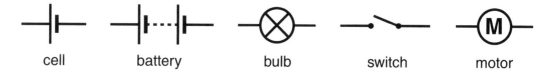

| cell | battery | bulb | switch | motor |

Forces are **pushes** and **pulls** that are shown as arrows on diagrams.
Magnets attract (pull) things made out of magnetic materials such as iron and steel. They can attract or repel (push) other magnets.

Examples of forces include:
- the Earth's pull – all objects are pulled towards the centre of the Earth;
- air resistance – the force from the air that acts against you, for example when you ride a bike;
- friction – this opposes slipping and sliding; it stops a car's wheels from slipping on the road and is also used by the brakes to slow the wheels down.

Pulling on a spring or an elastic band causes it to pull back and pushing down on the springs in a bed or a chair causes them to push back up.

All forces are measured in **newtons** using a **forcemeter**.

Lamps, stars and televisions are **light sources**, which means they can be seen because they give out light. Other objects are seen by the light that they **reflect**. When light meets a mirror it is reflected at the same angle at which it hits it, but most surfaces scatter light – they reflect it in all directions. We **see** things when light from them enters our eyes.

Sounds ...
- ... are caused when an object **vibrates**;
- ... travel as vibrations of the particles that make up materials;
- ... are detected by ears.

The **pitch** of a sound depends on the number of vibrations per second and the **loudness** depends on the size of the vibrations.

The **planets** in the **Solar System** orbit (go round) the **Sun**; **moons** orbit planets. A planet's **year** is the time it takes it to go once round the Sun. The **Earth** also turns on its axis, once each day. This causes day and night and makes the Sun appear to move across the sky, from East to West. The Moon's orbit of the Earth takes about 28 days.

Level 1 Describe changes caused by switching on a bulb and pushing or pulling objects. Recognise the source of sound or light.

Level 2 Compare the brightness of bulbs and the loudness and pitch of sounds. Compare speeds and directions of movement.

Level 3 Explain why a bulb does not light or why a sound can only be heard faintly. Explain how to change the speed or direction of movement of an object.

Level 4 Explain the effect of a switch in a circuit and the formation of shadows. Describe the effects of magnetic and gravitational forces and how the position of the Sun changes in the sky during a day.

Level 5 Explain how to change the current in a circuit and how to alter the pitch and loudness of a sound. Recognise when the forces on an object are balanced or unbalanced and describe how objects are seen. Use a model of the Solar System to explain the length of a day and a year.

Quick questions

Draw the circuit symbols for:

1   a cell   **2**   a bulb   **3**   a switch

Which of these forces is a push and which is a pull?

4   Your weight ....

5   The force between the North-seeking poles of two magnets ....

In a radio, a loudspeaker makes the sound.

6   How does the loudspeaker cone produce a sound?

....

7   How is it made to produce a louder sound?

....

How long does it take for:

8   the Earth to make one orbit of the Sun? ....

9   the Earth to turn once on its own axis? ....

10 the Moon to make one orbit of the Earth? ....

Instructions

Tests A and B should each take about 75 minutes.

Enter your start and finish times in the box at the beginning of each test.

You should take a short break halfway through the test.

Read all the words carefully. Look at any diagrams or pictures which should help you.

The questions for you to answer are in coloured boxes, for example:

Give the names of the parts of a flower shown in the picture.

Look for the to show you where to write your answer.

Remember to explain your answers if you are asked to do so.

After finishing a page, turn over to a new page without waiting to be told.

If a question is too hard, you should move on to the next question.

GOOD LUCK!

| START | |
| FINISH | |

Woodland view

1 The picture shows part of a wood.
On one tree there is a rope swing.

a Tick **two** boxes to show **two** things that both the bird and the tree can do.

fly ☐   grow ☐   lay eggs ☐

produce seeds ☐   reproduce ☐

b Tick **one** box to show **one** thing that both the bird and the swing can do.

grow ☐   move ☐   reproduce ☐

c Tick **two** boxes to show **two** reasons why few plants grow under the tree.

it is too dark ☐   it is too dry ☐

it is too light ☐   it is too wet ☐

2
Q1a

1
Q1b

2
Q1c

Max. 5
Q1
subtotal

15

The seal

1
Q2a

2 Here is a picture of a seal.
   a Why does the seal need to be able to swim?

....

1
Q2b

b Which part of its body does the seal use to push itself through the water?

....

1
Q2c

c Seals have a thick layer of fat underneath the skin. How does this help them to survive in the cold sea?

....

Growing plants from cress seeds

3 Adam and Jessie planted three lots of cress seeds and put them in different places.

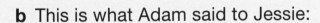

in a greenhouse   in a dark, warm cupboard   on a windowsill

a This is what Jessie said to Adam:

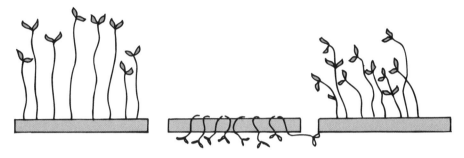

In the greenhouse, plants grow up towards the light. But on a windowsill, they grow sideways towards the light.

Is this true or false?

1
Q3a

....

b This is what Adam said to Jessie:

The plants in the cupboard would have grown better if you had watered them more.

Is this true or false?

1
Q3b

Max. 5
Qs 2–3
subtotal

....

Using a key

4 Here is a key. It can be used to identify four small animals.

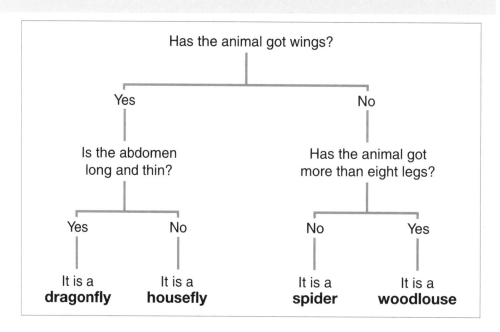

Has the animal got wings?

Yes | No

Is the abdomen long and thin? | Has the animal got more than eight legs?

Yes | No | No | Yes

It is a **dragonfly** | It is a **housefly** | It is a **spider** | It is a **woodlouse**

Here is a picture of a dragonfly.

2
Q4a

a Write down **two** things you could use to help identify a dragonfly.

....

....

2
Q4b

b Write down **two** things you could use to help identify a woodlouse.

....

....

c Rebecca finds an animal with eight legs and no wings. Use the key to work out what it is.

1
Q4c

....

d Rebecca reads that woodlice prefer to live in dark places rather than light places. What could she do to find out whether this is true?

2
Q4d

....

....

....

....

e Rebecca goes outside and finds woodlice underneath a stone, near a pond and in a piece of rotting wood. What else do woodlice like as well as darkness?

1
Q4e

....

Max. 8
Q4
subtotal

Parts of a flower

5 This question is about the parts of a flower and the job each part does.

a Write a label in each box using words from the list.

4
Q5a

ovary   petal   sepal   stamen   stigma

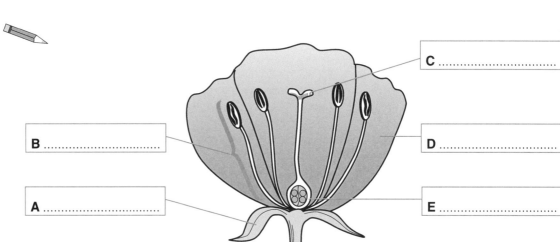

C ....

B ....

D ....

A ....

E ....

4
Q5b

b The table shows the jobs of the different parts of a flower.
Write the letter of the correct part of the flower next to each job.

Job	Letter of part
attracts insects to the plant	
male part of the flower	
where egg cells are made	
sticky part that receives pollen grains	
protects the flower when in bud	

21

Pulse rate

6 Sam is fitted with a device that records her pulse rate. The chart shows her pulse rate at playtime.

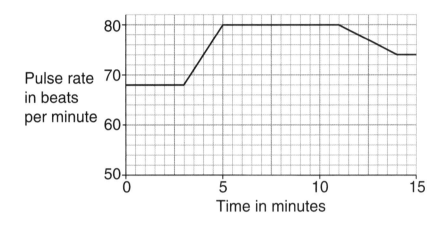

a What was Sam's pulse rate after five minutes?

1
Q6a

....

b After three minutes Sam started to run around. How can you tell this from the graph?

1
Q6b

....

c Why did Sam's pulse rate change when she started to run around?

1
Q6c

....

1
Q6d

d After how long did Sam's pulse rate start to go down again?

Max. 12
Qs 5–6
subtotal

....

In the kitchen

7 Ali and Alison are examining some objects they found in the kitchen.

a The table shows whether these objects can be bent easily and whether they are attracted to a magnet. Finish the table.

5
Q7a

Object	Is it easy to bend?	Is it attracted to a magnet?
newspaper	yes	no
polythene bowl	yes	no
wooden spoon		
marble egg cup		
kitchen foil		
candle		
steel knife		

b Which two objects are made of metal?

2
Q7b

....

c They find that the knife scratches the candle and the wooden spoon. The wooden spoon scratches the candle. Put the three objects in order of hardness. Put the hardest one first.

2
Q7c

....

Making coffee

8 Coffee can be made by pouring hot water onto crushed coffee beans. The diagram shows a machine for making coffee.

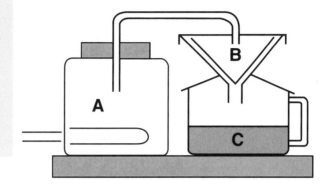

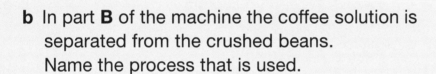

a In which part of the machine:

(i) is the water heated? ....

(ii) is the coffee solution collected? ....

(iii) does the coffee dissolve in the hot water?

....

3

Q8a
(i)–(iii)

b In part **B** of the machine the coffee solution is separated from the crushed beans.
Name the process that is used.

1

Q8b

....

c Instant coffee is made by spraying coffee solution onto heated rollers. Coffee granules are left on the rollers.

(i) Put a ring around the change that takes place on the rollers.

2

Q8c
(i)–(ii)

condensation   distillation   evaporation   melting

(ii) Is the change that takes place on the rollers reversible or non-reversible? Explain your answer.

Max. 15
Qs 7–8
subtotal

....

23

....

Which is the better insulator?

9 Rebecca and William want to find out which is the better heat insulator: fur or foam.

They pour boiling water into two beakers. One beaker has fur wrapped round it. The other one has foam wrapped round it. The temperature of the water is measured each minute. The diagram shows what they use.

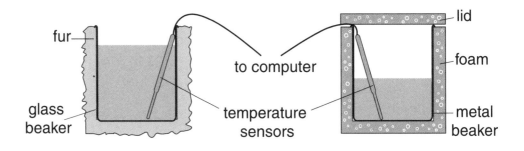

a What could they have used to measure the temperature of the water if they hadn't had temperature sensors?

....

b Write down **three** reasons why their test is not fair.

....

....

....

1
Q9a

3
Q9b

They repeat the experiment making sure this time that the experiment is fair. The computer draws graphs that show how the temperature of the water in the beakers changes. The graphs are shown here.

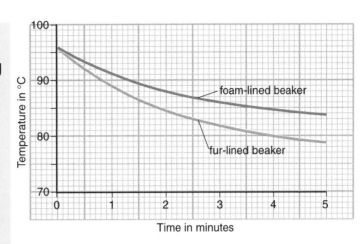

c What was the temperature of the water in the containers at the start of the experiment? .... °C

1
Q9c

d What was the temperature of the foam-lined container after 3 minutes? .... °C

1
Q9d

e What was the temperature of the fur-lined container after 3 minutes? .... °C

1
Q9e

f Three pupils, Sam, Chris and Jo, talk about the results. Sam says, 'Fur is the better insulator because animals use it.' Chris says, 'Fur and foam are both just as good because they start at the same temperature.' Jo says, 'Foam is better because the temperature is higher at the end.'

Who is correct, Sam, Chris or Jo?

1
Q9f

....

g How can you tell that this person is correct?

1
Q9g

Max. 9
Q9
subtotal

....

TAKE A SHORT BREAK

The water cycle

10 The drawing shows part of the water cycle.
The table below shows the five stages in the water cycle.

Finish the table by writing in numbers to show the order in which things happen. Number 1 has been written in for you.

3
Q10

water condenses to form clouds	
water runs into the sea	
water falls as rain	
water evaporates from the sea	1
water vapour rises in the air	

Cold drinks

11 Some ice cubes are placed in a glass of water.

1
Q11a

a What happens to the temperature of the water after the ice cubes are placed in the glass?

....

2
Q11b

b Explain why the outside of the glass becomes misty.

....

26

....

Bat and ball

12 Ahmed and Hayley are playing with a bat and ball.
Ahmed throws the ball and Hayley hits it back.

a Tick **two** things that change when Hayley hits the ball.

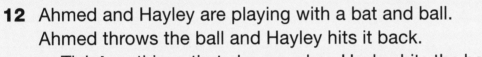

the colour of the ball ☐   the shape of the ball ☐

the direction of the ball ☐   the weight of the ball ☐

b Tick **two** things that change as the ball travels through the air.

the colour of the ball ☐   the speed of the ball ☐

the height of the ball ☐   the weight of the ball ☐

2
Q12a

2
Q12b

Max. 10
Qs
10–12
subtotal

Making a circuit

13 Chris makes this circuit.

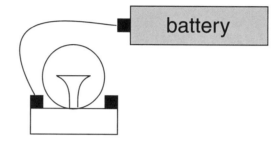

1
Q13a

a Why does the bulb not light?

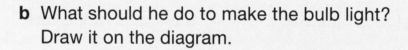

1
Q13b

b What should he do to make the bulb light?
Draw it on the diagram.

Sports day

14 On sports day, four runners line up to start a race.
They set off when they hear the noise from the starter.

Mary   Gutja

Sarong   Rose

a Who hears the loudest noise?

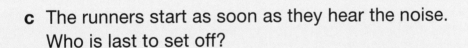

1
Q14a

b Explain why she hears the loudest noise.

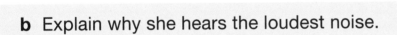

1
Q14b

c The runners start as soon as they hear the noise.
   Who is last to set off?

1
Q14c

1
Q14d

d Explain why she is last to set off.

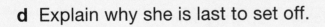

Max. 6
Qs
13–14
subtotal

Which is the strongest magnet?

15 A group of children have three magnets.

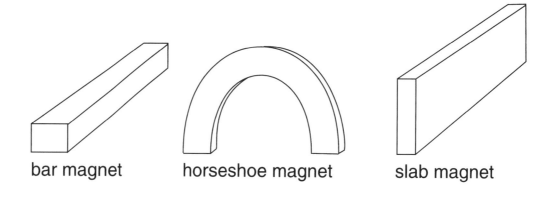

bar magnet   horseshoe magnet   slab magnet

They are trying to find out which is strongest.
They find that each magnet can pick up a drawing pin.

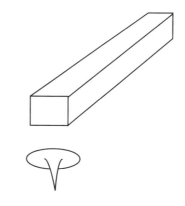

1
Q15a

a Draw an arrow to show the pull of the magnet on the drawing pin.

They find out how many drawing pins each magnet can pick up at a time.
Here are their results.

Magnet	Number of drawing pins
bar	28
horseshoe	23
slab	35

b Finish the bar chart. Draw a bar to show how many drawing pins each magnet picked up.

3
Q15b

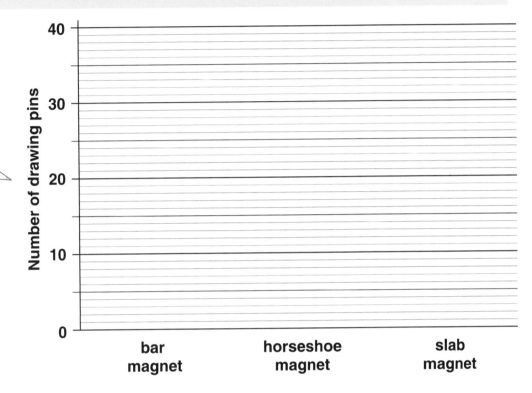

c Which magnet is strongest?

1
Q15c

....

It is the largest.

Tommy

It is the heaviest.

Terri

It picks up most drawing pins.

Toni

1
Q15d

d Each child has a different idea about why they think the magnet is strongest. Whose idea is correct?

....

Max. 6
Q15
subtotal

Travelling

16 A driver sets out early in the morning on a long journey. The Sun is low in the sky.

a The driver can see a puddle on the road.
Draw a line on the diagram to show how the driver can see the puddle.
Label your line with a **P**.

b During the journey, the position of the Sun in the sky changes. Draw a line on the diagram that shows the movement of the Sun during the morning.
Label the line **S**.

Earth, Sun and Moon

17 Benji is making a model of the Earth, Sun and Moon.
He uses a lamp for the Sun and a football for the Earth.

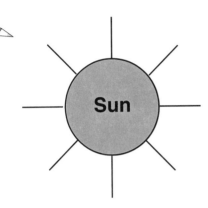

a Shade the part of the Earth that is in darkness.

b Benji wants to show his friend how day becomes
night. What should Benji do to show this?
Write below or draw on the diagram.

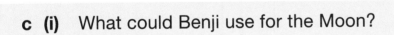

c (i) What could Benji use for the Moon?

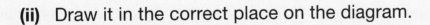

(ii) Draw it in the correct place on the diagram.

Lighting up

18 Petra makes this circuit. The bulb lights to its normal brightness.

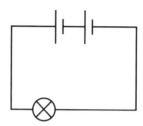

Describe the bulbs in each of the circuits below.
Use words from the list.

bright   **dim**   **normal**   **off**

A ....

B ....

C ....

D ....

4
Q18

Toy balloon

19 Daniel is holding a balloon.
The balloon is filled with helium.

What **two** things are pulling the balloon down?

....

....

Evaporation rate

20 Jack and Jill carried out an experiment to compare evaporation of water in different rooms in the school. They have four different sized containers available.

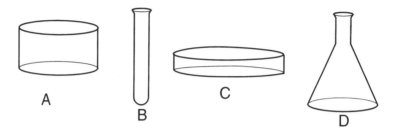

2
Q20a

a From which dish will the water evaporate fastest? Explain your choice.

....

....

They measure out 100 cm³ of water and pour it into container A.
They put it into a room where the temperature is 20°C. After four days they measure the volume of water left in the container.

They want to repeat the experiment in three other rooms where the temperatures are 15°C, 25°C and 30°C.

3
Q20b

b Write down **three** things they should do to ensure a fair test.

....

....

c The graph shows the results they obtained.

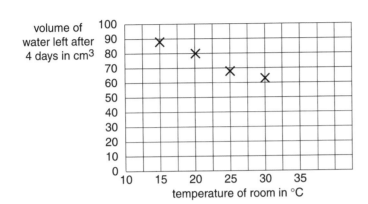

(i) What volume of water had evaporated at 20°C after four days?

1
Q20c(i)

....

(ii) What pattern can Jack and Jill see in their results?

2
Q20c(ii)

....

d They think the result at one temperature may be wrong.

(i) Which result do they think is wrong?

1
Q20d(i)

....

They did not make any mistakes measuring water volumes.

(ii) Suggest a reason why these results are wrong.

1
Q20d(ii)

Max.10
Q20
subtotal

....

Test B
Levels 3–5

START

FINISH

The pond

1 The drawing shows plants and animals around a pond.

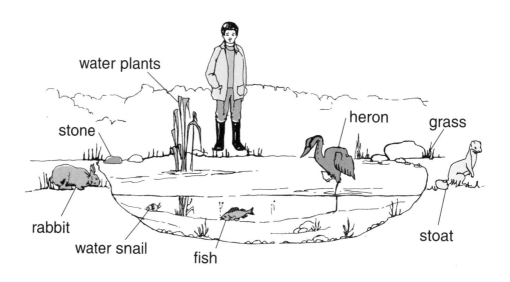

water plants

stone

heron

grass

rabbit

water snail

fish

stoat

3
Q1a

a Finish the table by writing the name of each thing in the correct column.

Non-living things	Living things
	water snail

b Write down **two** things that living things can do but non-living things cannot do.

....

....

Snails eat water plants.
Fish eat snails.

c Finish these two food chains using the things in the drawing.

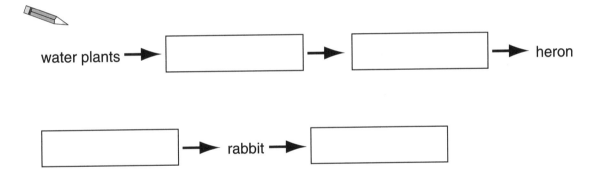

water plants ➤ [ ] ➤ [ ] ➤ heron

[ ] ➤ rabbit ➤ [ ]

d Write down the names of **two** producers shown in the drawing.

....

....

Teeth

2 The diagram shows the different teeth in your mouth.

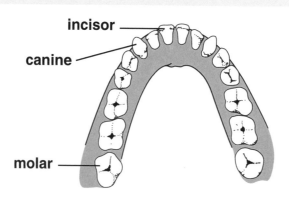

incisor

canine

molar

1
Q2a(i)

a (i) Which teeth rip or tear food?

....

1
Q2a(ii)

(ii) Which teeth grind food into small pieces?

....

1
Q2a(iii)

(iii) Which teeth cut food?

....

2
Q2b

b What **two** things can you do to keep your teeth healthy? Tick **two** boxes.

brush your teeth after meals ☐

drink lots of water ☐

eat lots of sweets ☐

visit the dentist regularly ☐

Organs in the body

3 The diagram shows some organs in the body.

  a Use words from the list to label the organs.

brain   **heart**   **lung**

A ....

B ....

C ....

  b Write in the table the name of each organ next to the job it does.

Job that the organ does	Organ
exchanges gases	
controls the body	
pumps blood	

  c What **two** jobs does the skeleton do?

....

....

  d What causes your bones to move when you walk?

....

Making bricks

4   People have made bricks from clay for many thousands of years.

Here are the steps:

> A   Leave to dry in sunlight.
> B   Shape the clay in a mould.
> C   Heat in an oven.
> D   Allow to cool.
> E   Dig out the clay from the ground.

a Put these statements in the correct order.
One has been done for you.

2
Q4a

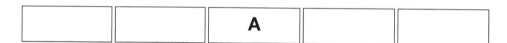

		A		

1
Q4b

b Is the change from clay to brick reversible or non-reversible? Explain your answer.

....

....

c Houses can be made of bricks or stone. Tick **two** reasons why bricks are better than stone for making houses.

bricks are easier to paint ☐

bricks are lighter ☐

bricks have regular shapes ☐

bricks are waterproof ☐

Here are some more materials that can be used for building a house. One of these materials is **natural** and the others have been **made**.

d Tick **one** box for each material to show if it is made or natural.

Material	Natural	Made
glass		
wood		
plastic		

Life cycle of a flowering plant

5 The diagram shows the stages in the life cycle of a flowering plant.

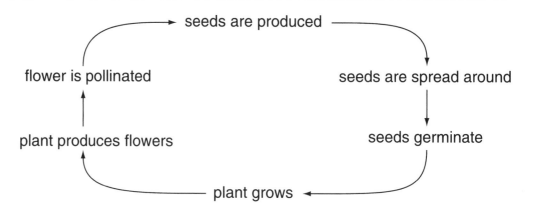

seeds are produced

flower is pollinated

seeds are spread around

plant produces flowers

seeds germinate

plant grows

1
Q5a

a Which stage is often done by insects?

1
Q5b

b What happens during germination?

2
Q5c

c Write down **two** conditions needed for seeds to germinate.

1
Q5d

d At which stage is pollen transferred to the stigma?

The Solar System

6 The Sun, the Earth and the Moon are three objects in the Solar System.

a Which object is the same shape as the Sun, Earth and Moon?

a tennis ball ☐   a 2p coin ☐

a 50p coin ☐   a breakfast cereal packet ☐

1
Q6a

Here are two pupils' ideas about the Sun, Earth and Moon:

Rosie: The Sun and the Moon both go round the Earth.
Rickie: The Earth and the Moon both go round the Sun.

b Who is correct?

....

1
Q6b

The diagram shows the position of the Sun early in the morning in summer.

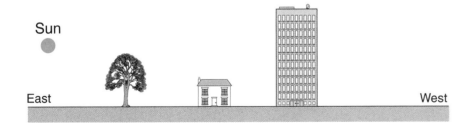
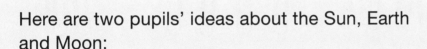

Sun

East   West

1
Q6c

1
Q6d

c Draw the position of the Sun at midday. Label this with an **M**.

Max. 9
Qs 5–6
subtotal

d Draw the position of the Sun in the evening, before sunset. Label this with an **E**.

Testing magnets

7 Some children are testing three magnets.

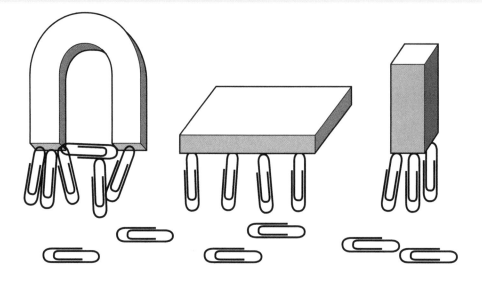

a What could they be trying to find out?
Tick **one** box.

Which magnet is heaviest. ☐

Which magnet points North. ☐

Which materials are attracted to a magnet. ☐

Which magnet is strongest. ☐

Which paper clips are strongest. ☐

b They test each magnet twice and record the results in a table.

Number of paper clips held by each magnet

	Horseshoe magnet	Slab magnet	Bar magnet
Test 1	23	17	19
Test 2	25	11	18

What **two** things should they do to make sure that the test is fair?

◆ 1
Q7b(i)

(i)

◆ 1
Q7b(ii)

(ii) ....

c Do the children have enough results to compare the magnets?
Tick **one** box.

◆ 2
Q7c

Yes ☐   No ☐

Explain your answer.

....

◆ 1
Q7d

d What should they do to be more certain about the results?

Max. 6
Q7
subtotal

....

TAKE A SHORT BREAK

Dissolving

8 Some children are testing different things to see which dissolve in water. Here are some of the things they test:

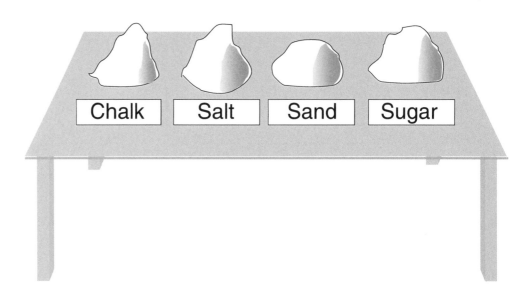

| Chalk | Salt | Sand | Sugar |

2
Q8a

a Put a ring round the **two** materials that dissolve in water.

1
Q8b

b How can they tell whether a material has dissolved in the water?

....

....

49

They then add some blue crystals to some cold water in a beaker.

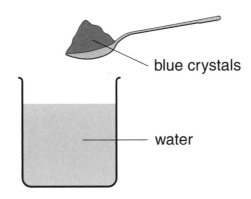

blue crystals

water

c Why does the water turn blue?

1

Q8c

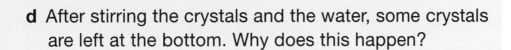

d After stirring the crystals and the water, some crystals are left at the bottom. Why does this happen?

1

Q8d

e How can they separate the crystals from the liquid?

1

Q8e

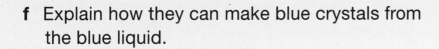

f Explain how they can make blue crystals from the blue liquid.

2

Q8f

Max. 8
Q8
subtotal

49

Misting up

9 Rosie parks her car outside her house. When she gets into her car on a cold morning she cannot see out of the windows because they are misted up.

a How do Rosie's car windows become misted up?

2
Q9a

....

....

....

b When Rosie switches on the air blower, the windows clear.
How does blowing air on the windows make them clear?

2
Q9b

....

....

Conducting electricity

10 Emma and Susan make this circuit to test which materials conduct electricity.

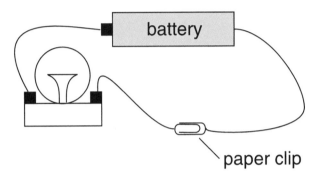

battery

paper clip

They leave a gap in the circuit, then fill the gap with different objects to do their test.

The bulb lights when a metal paper clip is placed in the gap.

Which other materials will cause the bulb to light? Put a tick or cross by each object in the table.

Object	Bulb lights (✓ or ✗)
metal paper clip	✓
plastic ruler	
brass screw	
wood block	

Snooker ball

11 A snooker ball bounces off a cushion.
   a Which diagram shows the force on the ball?
   Tick **one** box.

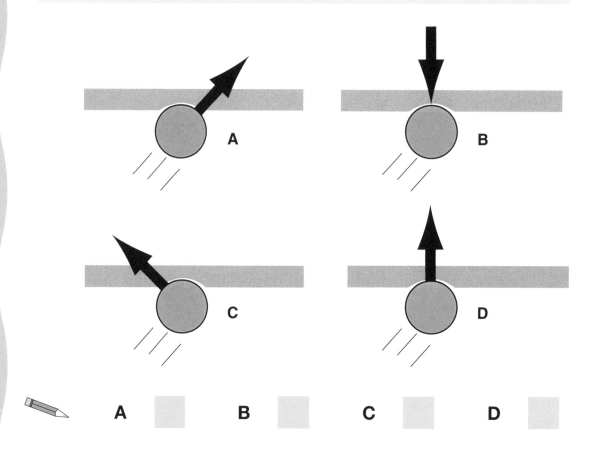

A ☐   B ☐   C ☐   D ☐

b Tick **two** boxes that show **two** things that change
when the ball bounces off the cushion.

the colour of the ball ☐

the direction of the ball ☐

the shape of the cushion ☐

the colour of the cushion ☐

1 Q11a

2 Q11b

Here comes the ice-cream van

Sam   **Tara**   **Ahmed**

12 Sam, Tara and Ahmed can all hear the sound from an ice-cream van.

a Who hears the loudest sound?

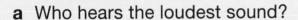

....

b Explain why this person hears the loudest sound.

....

....

1
Q12a

1
Q12b

Max. 5
Qs
11–12
subtotal

Batteries, bulbs and switches

13 Jill and Adam have made a circuit that lights three bulbs.

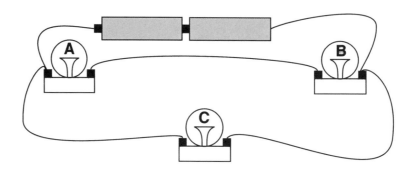

1
Q13a

Bulb **A** 'blows' and goes out.

a What happens to bulb **B**?

....

1
Q13b

b What happens to bulb **C**?

....

They then add three switches to their circuit.

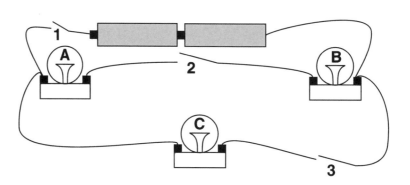

c In the box, draw a circuit diagram of Jill and Adam's circuit.

d Switch **1** is turned on. How many bulbs light?

....

e Switch **1** is kept on. Use ticks and crosses in the table below to show which bulbs are operated by switches **2** and **3**.

Switch	Bulbs operated		
	A	B	C
2			
3			

Max. 6
Q13
subtotal

Katie's pogo stick

14 Katie is given a new pogo stick for Christmas. Inside the pogo stick there is a large spring.

1
Q14a(i)

a (i) What happens to the spring when Katie sits on the pogo stick?

....

1
Q14a(ii)

(ii) Why does this happen?

....

2
Q14b

b Complete the sentences to describe the two forces acting on Katie. Use words from this list.

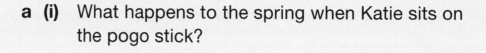

Earth   **pull**   **push**   **spring**

The downward force is the .... of the ....

The upward force is the .... of the ....

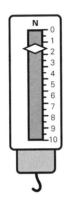

c The diagram shows a forcemeter.
What is the reading on the forcemeter?

2
Q14c

....

In the mirror

15 Sammy looks at her face in a mirror.

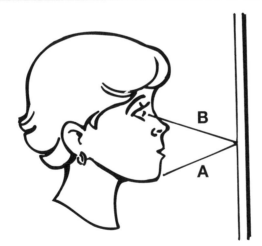

2
Q15a

a Draw one arrowhead on each of lines **A** and **B** to
show how the light travels.

1
Q15b

b Which word describes what happens to the light at
the mirror? Circle your choice.

Max. 9
Qs
14–15
subtotal

deflection   **inflection**   **reflection**   **refraction**

Making shadows

16 Tommy uses a torch and a cardboard shape to make a shadow picture on a wall.

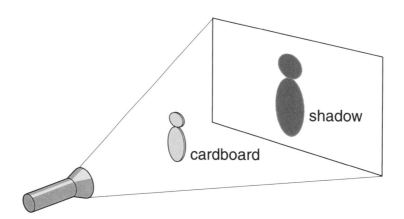

a Explain how the shadow is formed.

....

....

b Choose the best words from the list to complete the sentence.

becomes bigger   **becomes smaller**   **stays the same size**

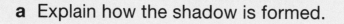

When the cardboard is moved nearer to the torch the

shadow ....

In the shadow

17 On a summer morning, Peter sits out in the garden.

a How does Peter stay cool?

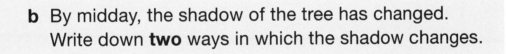

1
Q17a

b By midday, the shadow of the tree has changed. Write down **two** ways in which the shadow changes.

....

....

2
Q17b

2
Q17c

c Explain how the position of the Sun causes these changes. Give **two** reasons.

Max. 7
Qs
16–17
subtotal

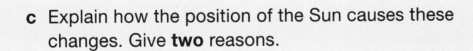

....

Growing tall sunflowers

2
Q18a

18 Chris and Asif have a competition to grow the tallest sunflower plants. They each sow seeds in the garden. Each week they measure the height of their sunflowers.

a Suggest **two** things that should be the same for each sunflower if the competition is to be fair.

....

....

They plot the results on a graph.

height of sunflower in cm

1
Q18b

b How high is Chris's sunflower after four weeks?

c What height might Asif's sunflower be after 10 weeks?

....

◆

1
Q18c

d Whose sunflower was taller after 7 weeks?

....

◆

1
Q18d

e When does Asif's sunflower grow fastest?
Tick the correct box.

0–1 week ☐   4–6 weeks ☐

2–3 weeks ☐   7–8 weeks ☐

◆

1
Q18e

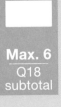

Max. 6
Q18
subtotal

Water and plant growth

19 How does water affect plant growth?

Some children are asked to find out the answer to this question.

a What should the children change in their investigation?

....

b What should the children keep the same in their investigation?

....

c What **two** things should the children measure and how should they measure them?

(i) ....

(ii) ....

....

1
Q19a

1
Q19b

1
Q19c(i)

1
Q19c(ii)

Max. 4
Q19
subtotal

62

Answers

HOW TO MARK THE TESTS

When marking the tests remember that the answers given are sample answers. You must look at your child's answers and judge whether they deserve credit. If they do, then award the mark.

You should pay special attention to spelling. There is no automatic penalty for a word that is misspelt. Look at the word as written and read it aloud. If it sounds correct and has the correct number of syllables, the mark can be awarded. For example, 'desolve' and 'weit' are acceptable for 'dissolve' and 'weight'. However, 'photosis' would not be accepted for photosynthesis.

Encourage the correct spelling of scientific words. Ask your child to look through this book and make a list of scientific words. Reviewing this list in the days before the tests is good preparation for your child.

It is sometimes difficult to know what children mean by their answers. Often, a vague use of the word 'it' can cause confusion. For example, if asked to explain how the experiment showed that Duvet C was warmest, a child may write 'it did not get very cold'. This answer does not make clear whether 'it' refers to Duvet C or the hot-water bottle that retained its heat longest when kept under Duvet C. An ambiguous answer must be marked wrong. When discussing these answers encourage your child to be very clear about what he/she means and to replace the word 'it' with the subject in full.

Above all, as you go through the test with your child, try to be positive. Look for good things that have been done in addition to resolving errors.

Enter your child's marks for each test on the Marking grid on page 79 and then work out his/her level of achievement on these tests on page 78.

QUICK QUESTIONS PAGES 9, 11, 13

Life processes and living things
1   Reproduction
2   Incisors
3   Blood
4   Skeleton
5   Root
6   Stem
7   Green plant or producer
8   Kidney
9   Glucose (sugar) and oxygen
10   Leaf

Materials and their properties
There may be alternative answers to Qs 1–5 but any correct answer should be based on properties.
1   Wood is not shiny *or* wood is not heavy *or* wood does not conduct electricity *or* wood does not conduct heat *or* wood breaks when it is bent.
2   Ice cannot be poured *or* ice has a fixed shape *or* ice is a solid.
3   Wood floats *or* steel is magnetic *or* steel is a metal.
4   Sand does not dissolve in water.
5   Water does not burn.
6   Melt
7   Condense
8   Burn
9   Melt
10   Reversible: 6, 7 and 9; non-reversible: 8

Physical processes

1

2

3

4 Pull
5 Push
6 By vibrating
7 By vibrating further/bigger vibrations
(NB *not* more vibrations)
8 One year
9 One day
10 28 days

Test A: Pages 15–37

1 a reproduce   *1 mark*
   grow   *1 mark*
  b move   *1 mark*

Note to parent

There are some characteristics of living things that are also characteristics of non-living things. The swing can move but it cannot reproduce.

  c It is too dark.   *1 mark*
   It is too dry.   *1 mark*

TOTAL 5 MARKS

2 a To catch fish   *1 mark*
  b Its tail   *1 mark*
  c It keeps them warm.   *1 mark*

Note to parent

This question is testing whether your child can recognise simple ways in which an animal is adapted to its environment. In **a**, do not award a mark for 'to move' or 'because it lives in the water'.

TOTAL 3 MARKS

3 a True   *1 mark*
  b True   *1 mark*

Note to parent

This question is testing whether your child is aware of the conditions needed for plant growth. As well as water and light, air and nutrients are also needed.

TOTAL 2 MARKS

4 a It has wings. *1 mark*
   It has a long, thin abdomen. *1 mark*
 b It does not have wings. *1 mark*
   It has more than eight legs. *1 mark*
 c A spider *1 mark*

In Key Stage 2 (KS2) your child is not expected to be able to construct a key, but is expected to be able to use one. In this question your child is asked to extract information from the given key. You could show your child pictures of the four animals and ask him or her to use the key to identify them.

 d Put some woodlice in a container where they can choose between a dark
   area or a light area. *1 mark*
   After leaving them for a while, count the number of woodlice in each area. *1 mark*
 e Damp *or* moisture *or* water *1 mark*

This question links with the type of practical activity that your child is likely to carry out in school and can do at home. If your child carries this out at home he/she should return the woodlice to where they were originally found after the investigation.

TOTAL 8 MARKS

5 a A: sepal
   B: stamen
   C: stigma
   D: petal
   E: ovary *4 marks*

Award four marks for all five correct in **a** and **b**, three marks for four correct, two marks for three correct and one mark if only one or two jobs have been identified correctly.

 b The completed table is:

Job	Letter of part
attracts insects to the plant	D
male part of the flower	B
where egg cells are made	E
sticky part that receives pollen grains	C
protects the flower when in bud	A

4 marks

TOTAL 8 MARKS

6 **a** 80 beats per minute   *1 mark*
   b Sam's pulse rate goes up.   *1 mark*
   c To pump more blood round her body   *1 mark*
   d After 11 minutes   *1 mark*

Note to parent

You could show your child how to measure his/her pulse rate using the pulse in the wrist or the neck. He/she could then investigate the effects that exercise and rest have on the pulse rate. As well as testing whether your child understands how these factors affect pulse rate, this question tests skills in reading data from a graph.

TOTAL 4 MARKS

7 **a** Here is the correctly completed table.

Object	Is it easy to bend?	Is it attracted to a magnet?
newspaper	yes	no
polythene bowl	yes	no
wooden spoon	no	no
marble egg cup	no	no
kitchen foil	yes	no
candle	no	no
steel knife	no	yes

5 marks
Award one mark for each line completed correctly.

   b Knife and kitchen foil   *2 marks*
   c Steel knife, wooden spoon, candle   *2 marks*
      Award one mark if steel knife is anywhere before wooden spoon, and one mark if wooden spoon is anywhere before candle.

TOTAL 9 MARKS

8 **a (i)** A   *1 mark*
   (ii) C   *1 mark*
   (iii) B   *1 mark*
   b filtering *or* filtration   *1 mark*
   c (i) evaporation   *1 mark*
   (ii) Reversible; the granules dissolve in water to make coffee solution *1 mark*

Note to parent

In KS2, children are often confused about the difference between sieving and filtration. *Sieving* uses a large mesh and can be used to separate large solid particles from smaller solid particles. It can also be used to separate large solid particles from a liquid. *Filtering* uses a much smaller mesh and so is used to separate small solid particles, such as powders, from a liquid. Also note that your child has to give the reason to gain a mark in **c(ii)**.

TOTAL 6 MARKS

9 a   A thermometer   *1 mark*
   b   One container has a lid, the other has no lid.   *1 mark*
      There are different amounts of water in the containers.   *1 mark*
      The containers are made of different materials.   *1 mark*
   c   96°C   *1 mark*

Note to parent   If your child has difficulty in interpolating graph scales, you can help by giving him/her more practice, but do not expect your child to take readings between divisions at this stage.

   d   86°C   *1 mark*
   e   82°C   *1 mark*
   f   Jo is correct.   *1 mark*

Note to parent   Foam is the better insulator because, although both beakers start at the same temperature, the foam-lined beaker has cooled less than the fur-lined one.

   g   After 5 minutes, the temperature of the foam-lined beaker is above 80°C (or a correct reading), the temperature of the fur-lined one is below 80°C (or a correct reading).   *1 mark*

TOTAL 9 MARKS

10   The completed table is:

water condenses to form clouds	3
water runs into the sea	5
water falls as rain	4
water evaporates from the sea	1
water vapour rises in the air	2

     3 marks

Award three marks for all four responses being correct, two marks for two or three correct responses and one mark for just one correct.

Note to parent   The important processes in the water cycle are evaporation and condensation. You can encourage your child to explain the water cycle to you using these terms correctly.

TOTAL 3 MARKS

11 a   It goes down   *1 mark*
   b   Water vapour from the air   *1 mark*
      condenses on the glass.   *1 mark*

 In KS2 children often find it difficult to appreciate that when water evaporates it changes to water vapour in the air. This water vapour condenses back into water on cold surfaces.

TOTAL 3 MARKS

12 a The direction of the ball   *1 mark*
          The shape of the ball   *1 mark*
b   The height of the ball   *1 mark*
          The speed of the ball   *1 mark*

 Forces on objects cause a change in shape. This is sometimes noticeable, for example the change in shape of a sagging bookshelf, and sometimes not noticeable, for example the change in shape of a concrete floor when you walk across it. Forces can also cause a change in the speed and/or direction of a moving object.

TOTAL 4 MARKS

13 a The circuit is not complete.   *1 mark*
b   Add another wire

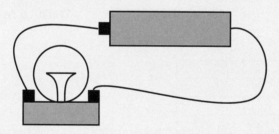

1 mark

 One of the first things that children learn about electricity in KS2 is that a complete circuit is needed for a device such as a bulb to work. Your child can practise making circuits at home using a few cheap and readily available components such as some batteries, bulbs, a motor and pieces of connecting wire. No special kit is needed.

TOTAL 2 MARKS

14 a   Rose   *1 mark*
  b   She is closest to the starter.   *1 mark*
  c   Mary   *1 mark*
  d   She hears the sound last.   *1 mark*

Children can be made aware that sound takes a finite time to travel by drawing their attention to events where they see something happening before they hear it. A low-flying aircraft is one example of such an event.

TOTAL 4 MARKS

15 a   The arrow should point vertically upwards.   *1 mark*
  b   Here is the finished bar chart.

3 marks
Award one mark for each bar drawn correctly.

  c   The slab magnet   *1 mark*
  d   Toni   *1 mark*

Questions where your child has to pick out correct ideas about experiments are very common. Encourage your child to talk about each of the possibilities.

TOTAL 6 MARKS

16 a   The line should come from the Sun, be reflected at the puddle,
and then go up towards the driver's eye line.   *1 mark*
It should bounce off the puddle at the same angle as it hits.   *1 mark*

Your child should appreciate that most objects are seen by the light that they reflect. Mirrors and other shiny surfaces reflect light in a regular and predictable way. Other objects are said to *scatter* the light; they reflect it in all directions.

b   The line should show the Sun moving higher in the sky.   *1 mark*
           It should move to the right, following a curved path.   *1 mark*

TOTAL 4 MARKS

17 a

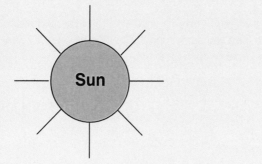

1 mark

b   He should turn the Earth round on its own axis.   *1 mark*

Your child may not use this form of words, but make sure that he/she is clear about the different movements of the Earth. One *rotation* on its axis takes one day and causes day and night. One *orbit* round the Sun takes one year.

c (i)   Award a mark for any object that is spherical and smaller than the Earth,
          for example a tennis ball or table tennis ball.   *1 mark*
   (ii)   It should be drawn much closer to the Earth than to the Sun.   *1 mark*

TOTAL 4 MARKS

18   A: normal   *1 mark*
         B: dim   *1 mark*
         C: off   *1 mark*
         D: dim   *1 mark*

The bulb in **C** is off because the cells are connected back-to-back, so there is no voltage and no current.

TOTAL 4 MARKS

19   Daniel   *1 mark*
        and the Earth   *1 mark*

Children at all levels are easily confused about gravitational forces. Emphasise to them that it is the Earth that pulls things towards it and not some unseen object called 'gravity'.

TOTAL 2 MARKS

20 a	C		*1 mark*
	The largest area of water open to the room.		*1 mark*
b	Same volume of water		*1 mark*
	Same shape container		*1 mark*
	Left for the same time		*1 mark*
c (i)	20 cm³		*1 mark*
(ii)	As temperature rises, more water evaporates (or the volume of water left decreases).		*2 marks*
d (i)	25°C		*1 mark*
(ii)	Temperature of the room changes/room warms up		*1 mark*

Note to parent

Part **b** involves your child understanding fair testing. In **c(i)** the common error is to give the volume from the graph, i.e. 80 cm³. This is the volume of water remaining. It has to be taken away from 100 cm³ to get the volume that had evaporated. In **d(ii)** your child has to carry out a simple evaluation of why an experiment might go wrong.

TOTAL 10 MARKS

TEST TOTAL 100 MARKS

Test B: Pages 38–62

1 a	Non-living: stone		*1 mark*
	Living: water plants, person, heron, grass, stoat, fish, water snail, rabbit		*2 marks*
	Allow one mark if one living thing is omitted or placed in the wrong column.		
b	*Any two from:* feed, sense, respire (*allow* breathe), grow, get rid of waste, reproduce and move		*2 marks*

Note to parent

Do not worry if your child does not know all the characteristics of living things. At KS2 the ones required are feed, move (animals only), grow and reproduce.

c	snail (*1 mark*), fish (*1 mark*)		*2 marks*
	grass (*1 mark*), stoat (*1 mark*)		*2 marks*
d	grass		*1 mark*
	water plants		*1 mark*

Note to parent

Your child should be aware that green plants are the producers in a food chain. They are called producers because they make their own food. All the other organisms in the food chain rely on this food.

TOTAL 11 MARKS

2 a (i) canines   *1 mark*
   (ii) molars   *1 mark*
  (iii) incisors   *1 mark*
    b Brush your teeth after meals   *1 mark*
       Visit the dentist regularly   *1 mark*

TOTAL 5 MARKS

Your child is required to know the jobs of the three types of teeth. Children should be able to find examples of the three types of teeth in their mouth.

3 a A: brain   *1 mark*
       B: heart   *1 mark*
       C: lung   *1 mark*
    b Here is the completed table.

Job that the organ does	Organ
exchanges gases	lung
controls the body	brain
pumps blood	heart

Award one mark for each correct organ.   *3 marks*

    c It supports   *1 mark*
       and protects the body.   *1 mark*
    d Muscles   *1 mark*

TOTAL 9 MARKS

Children working at Level 4 should be able to identify the major organs in the body. At Level 5, they should be able to describe the jobs that these organs do.

4 a The correct order is:
       E B A C D   *2 marks*
       Award two marks if fully correct and one mark if two are correct.
    b Non-reversible – the bricks (or brick dust) do not make clay if mixed
       with water   *1 mark*

To gain the mark in **b**, your child needs to give a correct reason as well as the correct answer.

c Bricks are lighter. *1 mark*
Bricks have regular shapes. *1 mark*

d Here is the completed table.

Material	Natural	Made
glass		✓
wood	✓	
plastic		✓

3 marks
Award one mark for each correct row.

Your child should be able to classify a range of materials as made or natural. Many natural materials are in short supply or have inferior properties to made materials and are being replaced by materials that are made, i.e. where the natural material has been processed to change its properties.

TOTAL 8 MARKS

5 a pollination *1 mark*
b The seeds sprout. *1 mark*
c Any two from: warmth/moisture/damp/water/air/oxygen *2 marks*
d pollination *1 mark*

Your child should be able to link the correct scientific names to each of the stages in the life cycle of a flowering plant. Wild flowers or flowers from a garden can be dissected without using special tools to study the different parts of a flower.

TOTAL 5 MARKS

6 a a tennis ball *1 mark*
b Rickie *1 mark*
c The Sun, labelled M, should be drawn between the house and the skyscraper, above the roof level of the skyscraper. *1 mark*
d The Sun should be drawn in a similar position in the sky, but on the right-hand side of the page. *1 mark*

If the opportunity exists, look with the child at the position of the Sun in the sky during the day. Use a compass to identify north, south, east and west.

TOTAL 4 MARKS

7 a Which magnet is strongest. *1 mark*

   b Use paper clips that are all the same mass/weight/size. *1 mark*

       Make sure that all the paper clips are made from iron/are magnetic. *1 mark*

   c No. *1 mark*

       Both tests show different numbers of paper clips for each magnet. *1 mark*

       They cannot be certain about the results for the slab magnet. *1 mark*

 **Note to parent**

No mark is awarded here for ticking a box. Credit is awarded for identifying the variability in the data for each magnet, and that the data for the slab magnet shows more variability than that for the others.

   d Carry out more tests until they can see a clear pattern. *1 mark*

TOTAL 6 MARKS

8 a salt *1 mark*

       sugar *1 mark*

   b The water is clear *or* there is no material left at the bottom. *1 mark*

   c The blue crystals have dissolved. *1 mark*

   d No more will dissolve. *1 mark*

   e By filtering *1 mark*

   f Heat the liquid *or* leave it in a warm place *1 mark*

       so that the water evaporates. *1 mark*

 **Note to parent**

Dissolving substances and making crystals are science tasks that your child can carry out at home with no special equipment. Alum is a suitable substance for your child to use for crystal growing.

TOTAL 8 MARKS

9 a There is water vapour in the air. *1 mark*

       This condenses on the windows. *1 mark*

   b The water evaporates. *1 mark*

       The air takes away the water vapour. *1 mark*

 **Note to parent**

It is worth emphasising to your child that washing dries quicker on a windy day than on a calm day, because the wind removes the water vapour from around the washing.

TOTAL 4 MARKS

10

Object	Bulb lights (✓ or ✗)
metal paper clip	✓
plastic ruler	✗
brass screw	✓
wood block	✗

3 marks
Award one mark for each correct row.

Note to parent Children are often confused about electricity and magnetism. They frequently think that all metals conduct electricity and all metals are magnetic. One important property of metals is that they do conduct electricity, but of the common metals only iron, nickel and steel are magnetic.

TOTAL 3 MARKS

11a   B   *1 mark*

Note to parent   Diagram B is the only one that shows a force acting on the ball.

b   The direction of the ball   *1 mark*
         The shape of the cushion   *1 mark*

TOTAL 3 MARKS

12 a   Sam   *1 mark*
b   He is closest to the ice-cream van.   *1 mark*

TOTAL 2 MARKS

13 a   It goes out.   *1 mark*
b   It stays lit *or* nothing happens.   *1 mark*
c   *1 mark*

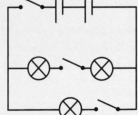

d   None   *1 mark*

e The completed table is:

Switch	Bulbs operated		
	A	B	C
2	✓	✓	✗
3	✗	✗	✓

2 marks
Award one mark for each correct row.

For this mark to be awarded your child has to draw a complete circuit with the correct symbols. These are found on page 12 at the front of this book.

TOTAL 6 MARKS

14 a (i) It is squashed *or* gets smaller.   *1 mark*
   (ii) There is a force pushing down on it.   *1 mark*
   b pull; Earth   *Both words required.*   *1 mark*
       push; spring   *Both words required.*   *1 mark*

It is not only at KS2 that children find forces difficult. The best approach is to teach that forces are caused by objects and act on other objects, so all forces can be described as 'object A pulls/pushes object B'. Use of the term 'gravity' is confusing; it leads children to talk about gravity as if it were an object. The downward force that acts on objects is best described as 'the Earth's pull'.

c Answer is $1\frac{1}{2}$ or 1.5   *1 mark*
   newtons or N   *1 mark*

TOTAL 6 MARKS

15 a The arrowhead on A should point to the mirror.   *1 mark*
       The arrowhead on B should point to the eye.   *1 mark*

Children's confusion about seeing is often due to them thinking that eyes give out light. You can explain to them that light is only given out by light sources such as lamps and television screens. Other objects are seen by the light that they reflect.

b reflection   *1 mark*

TOTAL 3 MARKS

16 a The light does not pass through the cardboard. *1 mark*
  b It becomes bigger. *1 mark*

Children can enjoy learning about shadows by making a shadow puppet theatre. All that is needed is some cardboard, a battery and a torch lamp.

TOTAL 2 MARKS

17 a By sitting in the shadow *1 mark*
  b It becomes shorter. *1 mark*
    It changes position. *1 mark*
  c The Sun is higher in the sky. *1 mark*
    The Sun has moved across the sky. *1 mark*

A much better answer to **c** is that the Sun seems to have moved across the sky or the Earth has rotated on its axis.

TOTAL 5 MARKS

18 a Two from: same soil, same amount of water, same light conditions *2 marks*
  b Any answer between 30 and 32 cm *1 mark*
  c Either 84 or 85 cm *1 mark*
  d Asif's *1 mark*
  e 4–6 weeks *1 mark*

In **c** any answer between 83 cm and 87 cm is acceptable. In **e** your child needs to realize that the plant is growing faster when the graph is steeper.

TOTAL 6 MARKS

19 a The amount of water given to each plant. *1 mark*
  b Where the plants are kept. *1 mark*

A mark is awarded here for an answer that shows that all the plants used in the investigation should be subject to the same changing physical conditions of light and temperature or any other factor that could affect plant growth.

  c The volume of water given to each plant, using a measuring jug or cylinder. *1 mark*
    The height of each plant, using a ruler. *1 mark*

The weight or mass of each plant is not awarded any credit here, as this would also include the weight of the water given to the plants.

TOTAL 4 MARKS

TEST TOTAL 100 MARKS

Determining your child's level

FINDING YOUR CHILD'S LEVEL IN TESTS A AND B

When you have marked a test, enter the total number of marks your child scored for each question on the Marking grid overleaf. Then add them up and enter the test total on the grid.

Using the total for each test, look at the chart below to determine your child's level.

Test A or Test B

Level 2 or below	Level 3	Level 4	Level 5	Gifted & Talented
up to 20	21–35	36–65	66–87	88+

FINDING YOUR CHILD'S OVERALL LEVEL IN SCIENCE

After you have worked out separate levels for Tests A and B, add up your child's total marks for the two tests. Use this total and the chart below to determine your child's overall level in Science. The chart also shows you how your child's level in these tests compares with the target level for his/her age group.

Total for Tests A and B

Level 2 or below	Level 3	Level 4	Level 5	Gifted & Talented
up to 40	41–70	71–130	131–174	175+
Working towards target level for age group		Working at target level	Working beyond target level	